A Guide To

Easter

Collectibles

Juanita Burnett

A Guide To

Easter

Collectibles

COLLECTOR BOOKS
A Division of Schroeder Publishing Co., Inc.

The current values in this book should be used only as a guide. They are not intended to set prices, which vary from one section of the country to another. Auction prices as well as dealer prices vary greatly and are affected by condition as well as demand. Neither the Author nor the Publisher assumes responsibility for any losses that might be incurred as a result of consulting this guide.

Searching For A Publisher?

We are always looking for knowledgeable people considered to be experts within their fields. If you feel that there is a real need for a book on your collectible subject and have a large comprehensive collection, contact us.

COLLECTOR BOOKS
P.O. Box 3009
Paducah, Kentucky 42002-3009

Printed by IMAGE GRAPHICS, INC., Paducah, Kentucky

Dedication

This book is dedicated to my readers, my friends, my family, and people everywhere who love Easter.

Acknowledgments

I would like to thank the following collectors who have shared so generously their collections and also their knowledge.

Ginger Edson
Donna and Bob Lockward
Jean Marshall

In varying ways the following people were helpful and I want to say thank you.

Early J. Burgess
Tim Burnett
Vada Horner
Cathy and Terri Nell
Rema Padgett
Patricia Robarts
Al Snapp

A special thank you to my photographer, Jeannette Petty.

Finally, I would like to express my sincere appreciation to the staff at Harmon's Photo and to anyone who has in any way made a contribution to this book.

Contents

Preface

In the past few years, there has been an increased interest in Easter collectibles and rightly so as Easter decorating ranks second only to Christmas.

Eggs, bunnies, chicks and baskets filled with spring grass are the most popular items used in our decorating. The older, more interesting examples are vigorously sought by today's collectors.

The new Easter collectibles are being snapped up also. For example if you want an Annalee Bunny, shop early. In season the shops have a large selection. There are, to name a few, handmade bunnies in adult clothes, papier-maché eggs, tins and Easter trees with all the trim. These will surely delight tomorrow's collector. Whether you collect old or new, or both, collecting Easter items can bring much pleasure and brighten your Easter festivities.

It is my sincere wish that you, the reader, find this book both enjoyable and informative, and the pleasure was mine.

History Of Easter

The name *Easter* comes from Anglo-Saxon *Eostre*, a goddess of light or spring whose festival was celebrated in April. The proper time for celebrating Easter was long in dispute. Finally, in 325 A.D. the Council of Nice fixed Easter as the first Sunday after the full moon which appears on or after March 21st.

In ancient Egypt, the hare was the symbol for fertility and was considered sacred. Some writings imply that the hare was the earthly form of the goddess Easter. The Easter hare is thought to have originated in Germany, and many of our older Easter collectibles were also made there. The word *hare* was translated to *rabbit* in 19th century America and is a modern day descendant of the Pennsylvania-German *Oschter Haws.*

Eggs have long been the symbol of new life, and the custom of sending Easter eggs is thought to have originated with the Persians. In those days eggs were scarce and the gift of an egg was gratefully received. As they became more plentiful, people began to color them for their spring festivals. Several reasons have been given for coloring them; one to fulfill the longing for bright colors as spring arrived after the long winter, and another was the colors suggested joy. It became customary to give fancy, highly decorated eggs; some were decorated with gold and precious stones. In many European countries egg decorating became a fine art. The most famous eggs are those designed in Russia and Poland. Carl Faberge, goldsmith for the Russian Imperial Court, was a designer who crafted his first classic Easter egg complete with diamonds and rubies in 1886. Today, most of his designs are in museums and there are less than sixty known to exist.

The Russian Imperial Court's fondness for Easter eggs had much influence and many decorative objects took their form, such as doorbells, bell-cord knobs, and containers.

Hiding, eating, and exchanging Easter eggs is a popular custom in many countries. Chicken eggs are most commonly used. The eggs are hard boiled and dyed in various colors. Before commercial dye was available, vegetable juices were used (beets, spinach, onion peel, etc). Children sometimes roll eggs in a race against one another; the egg that stays uncracked the longest is the winner. In some areas the Easter Bunny fills the bonnets, caps or baskets with colored eggs.

During the term of President James Madison, children were allowed to roll eggs on the Capital grounds. This continued except for the Civil War period. Later when officials decided it was ruining the grass, Mrs.

Hayes, wife of President Rutherford Hayes, saved the game by allowing the children to have their egg roll on the White House lawn. Today the tradition continues for youngsters twelve and under.

Chocolate bunnies can be traced back to the 1850's in Germany when candy factories produced rabbits, eggs, chickens, as well as other confections. This soon spread to other European countries and eventually to the United States. The tradition of giving Easter chocolates has endured and today is a big business.

In the United States, Easter greeting postcards grew very popular in the early 20th century. The postcards with rabbits dressed in clothing are the most prized. Next are those with children and also the ones with chicks. The hold-to-light postcards are scarce and much more valuable.

Decorations for the Easter holiday were widely available by 1913. There were a variety of rabbits, papier-maché eggs, candy containers, cotton chicks, etc. By the second half of the 19th century, Easter became a commercial event in the United States.

In the mid 1930's, the toy makers saw the potential for Easter related toys. This new market enabled them to keep their workers employed year round. There were pull toys, tin rabbits, ducklings and eggs. By this time Japan and other countries had entered the marketplace. This market is still strong today. The styles and materials have changed over the years. The tin gave way to plastic, but our desire for Easter related items is stronger than ever.

There have been many changes in the evolution of Easter customs and decorations, but one thing has not changed: the beauty of the season makes the heart sing!

Tips On Dating Your Collection

In the early 1900's, there was a wide variety of papier-maché and composition Easter items on the market. Many of these older examples were imported from Germany.

The older rabbits have a serious expression on their faces. Many styles had elongated bodies.

Stuffed rabbits were dressed in human clothing fashioned from felt, cotton, and silk. Their bodies were made of mohair, felt, and velveteen. These were filled with straw, cellulose, cotton and by the 1950's, many forms of synthetic foam were used. Today the body material is chiefly plush synthetics with polyester stuffing.

Many of the older maché eggs have a loop for hanging. The scenes were simpler than those of today. Sawtooth paper lace encircled the interior. The oldest eggs were filled with fancy paper to cushion the Easter gifts enclosed.

To date the German marked pieces:
German – before 1918
German Republic – 1918–1933
East Germany or German Democratic Republic – After World War II
West Germany or the Federal Republic of Germany – After World War II

To date anything that is labeled:
Large city, state, no zone number – before 1943
Zone number – 1943–1963
Present full 5 digit zip code – 1963 to present

Cleaning And Sanitizing

Before bringing some cloth objects into your home you may feel they need to be sanitized. Spray lightly with Lysol Disinfectant Spray. Don't attempt to clean unless absolutely necessary. However, if they are badly soiled, Woolite Upholstery Cleaner may be used. I suggest shaking the container throughly, then spraying into a clean cloth. Next, wipe the object with the cloth rather than spraying directly on the object. You may flluff with a clean towel. When dry, spray lightly with Lysol Disinfectant Spray.

Care and Storage

Unless you are going to display your collection year round, it must be carefully stored. First you will need good, sturdy packing boxes. Cardboard milk boxes from the grocery are fine, or you may want to invest in storage containers. Wrap each article seperately in tissue paper. Some of the smaller metal or plastic eggs may fit into your discarded egg cartons. If possible, when your collection has grown, it maybe helpful to separate the items per container. For instance, all chalk items in a box, all metal items in a separate box. This will ensure that a heavier object would not rest on a lighter weight object and cause damage.

Finally, label each container as to contents and store in a cool, dry area. Extremes in temperature can cause damage.

Rabbits

Pair boy rabbits, American, 1940's.

Left: Steiff "Nikki," German, 1940's.
Right: Musical wind-up, 1950's.

Easter Parade Girl Bunny, American,
Annalee, 1980's (736 produced).

Left: Jockey rabbit, 1930's. Right: Scottish attire, 1940's.

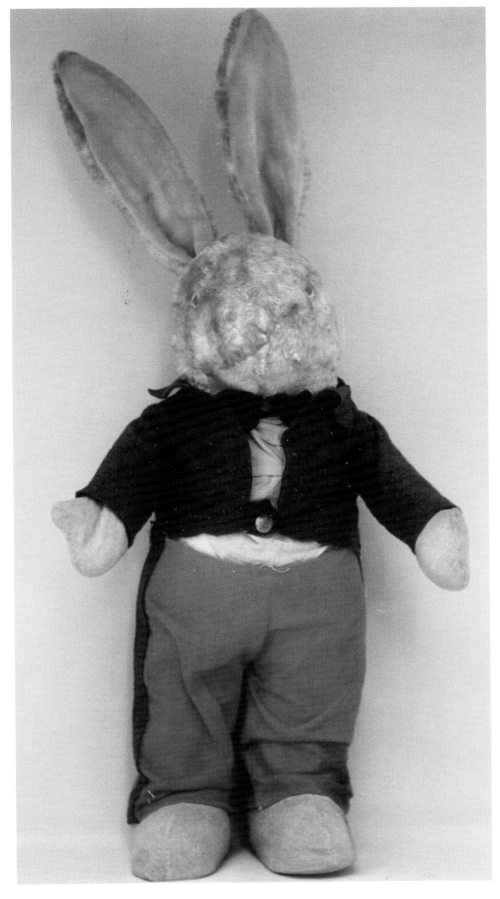

Straw stuffed, felt clothes, 1930's.

Sunny Bunny Doll, felt clothes, early 1900's.

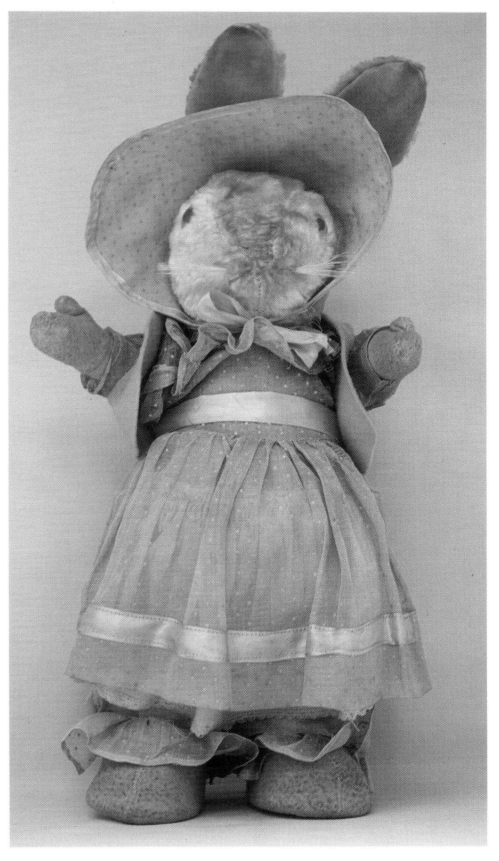

Mohair and cotton suede, 1930's.

Plush, long ears with wire, 1950's.

Pair handmade rabbits, sewn from old embroidered scarfs, 1990.

Handcrafted from 1930's upholstery fabric, button eyes.

Left: Knickerbocker Toy Co., Inc., 1960's. Middle: Snap corduroy, 6¼", limbs snap, made in China, 1983. Right: Cotton flannel rabbit, Japanese, 1950's.

Mohair, felt clothes, 1950's.

Cotton suede, hand stitched features, 1940–1950.

Left: Plush 29", 1950–1960's. Right: Plush, 19", attached "Happy Easter" card, 1960's.

Straw stuffed, felt clothes, 1930's.

Mohair, glass eyes, 1920's.

Felt clothes, 1940's.

Bride and groom, handmade clothes of silk and cotton, composition shoes, early 1900's.

Straw stuffed rabbit and cart, turn of the century.

Left: Plush, made by Gund Mfg. Co., 1940 – 1950's.
Right: Plush, cotton string whiskers, felt features, Common Wealth Toy Co., 1950–1960.

Left: Plush, Huron Products. Middle: Gibson Greeting, Inc.
Right: Jointed arms and legs, S. D. F. Dolls. All 1980's.

Handcrafted gentlemen rabbits, 1980's.

Squeak toy, mohair, German, early 1900's.

Cotton rabbits, 1930–1940's.

Velveteen rabbit, 1930's.

Straw stuffed, 1940's.

Left: 7" Boy Bunny. Middle: 7" Ballerina. Right: 7" Girl Bunny. All made by Annalee, 1980's.
Left has been redressed (lost value).

Left: Fur head, glass eyes, 1920's.
Right: Felt clown, celluloid feet, 1920's.

Cowboy, 1950's.

Left: Mohair, 1930's. Right: Mohair, turn of the century.

Plush, rubber head, My Toy Co., 1950's.

Handcrafted from printed fabric kits (still available).
Left: 1950 – 1960. Right: 1970's.

Handcrafted lady, 1980's.

Plush, felt clothes, 1940's.

Straw stuffed, 1940's.

Candy containers. Left: Foxy Grandpa on mohair rabbit, 1920's.
Middle: Mohair rabbit, wax face, 1900. Right: Happy Hooligan, 1920.

German, 1940's.

Candy container, 1910–1920's.

Candy container, rooster's head comes off,
rabbit is a nodder, 8½", early 1900's.

Candy container, flocked, German, 12", 1950's.

Candy containers, early 1900's.

Candy containers, American, 1940's.

Composition, original basket on back, 1930–1940's.

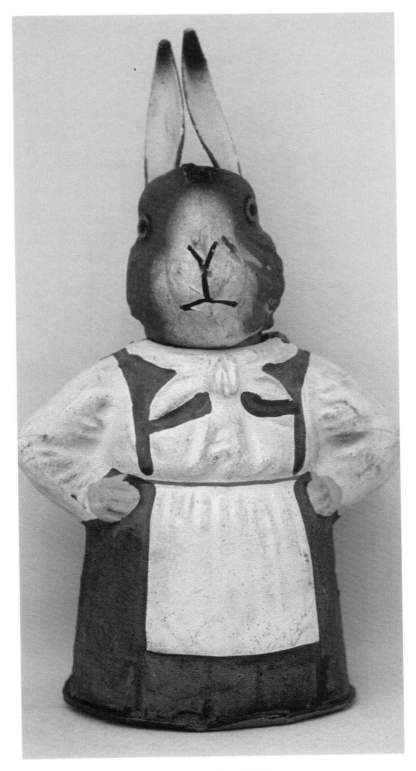

Candy container, 1920's.

Candy container, 1930–1940's.

Papier-maché rabbit, moss cart, cotton chicks, German, 1930's.

Candy containers, German, 1930–1940's.

Left: Mohair rabbit pops up and down in cabbage, wind-up, French, early 1900.
Right: Mohair rabbit, composition arms, lead feet, wind-up, 1880–1890.

45

Rabbit candy container and stick cart, German, early 1900's.

All German, early 1900's.

Candy containers. Left: 9", 1940's. Middle: 11", 1940's. Right: 9", 1940's.

Roly poly candy containers. Left: Mohair, celluloid face, 1900–1920's.
Right: Papier-maché, glass eyes, German, 1920.

Cardboard rabbits, 5", 1940's.

Gold rabbit, 1920's. Cart, early 1900's.

48

Early 1900's.

Left: Cotton felt rabbit on papier-maché, 1920's.
Right: Candy container, 1920's.

Composition, 1940's.

Candy container, early 1900's.

Bank, felt skirt, marked Roy Des of Fla., 1968.

Celluloid, wind-ups, Japanese, 1940's.

Candy container, 1940–1950.

Banks, flocked, made in Hong Kong, 1960–1970's.

Celluloid, 1920–1930's.

Bank, plush ears, Roy Des of Fla., 1976.

Celluloid, 1920–1930's.

Candy containers, seperate below neckline, 1950's.

Bank, early plastic, 1930–1940's.

Celluloid roly polys, Japanese, 1920's.

Copy from old mold, 1980's.

Dinner bell, 1970's.

Left: Marked U. S. A., 1930's. Middle: Napco, 1960. Right: Marked U.S. A., 1930's.

Glass candy containers. Left and right: J. H. Millstein Co., 1940's. Middle: Reproduction, recent.

Left: German bisque, 1920's. Right: Japanese, 1940's.

Handcrafted replica of original carving, by Red Mill Mfg., Inc., 1980's.

Handcrafted, 15", 1920–1930's.

Molds, early 1900's, as found condition.

Left: Handcrafted rabbit, 15¼", limbs move, 1970-1980. Right: cutout.

64

Handcrafted rabbit and cart, 1940's.

Assorted chalk rabbits, 1930–1940's.

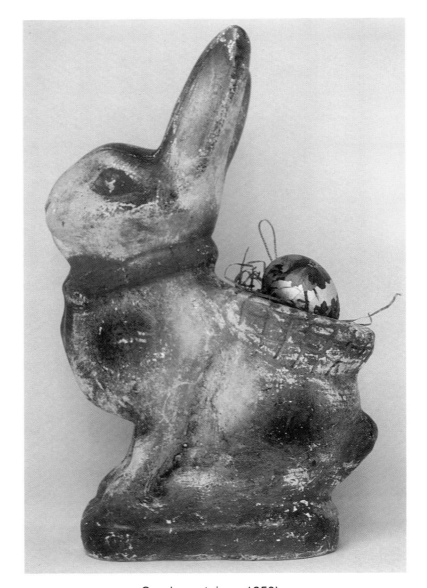

Candy container, 1950's.

Assorted chalk rabbits.

Pull Toys

Left: 1920's. Right: 1930's.

Lehmann "Duo," German, circa 1900.

Handcrafted, 1980's.

Wood rabbit, cardboard cart, 1940's.

Penny toys, 1880–1900. Metal egg, early 1900's.

Handcrafted, 1930's.

Maché rabbit, 1940's.

Wind-Ups

Plastic rabbit on metal tricycle, 1970's.

Fabric bodies, composition feet, 1930's.

Strutting Bunny by Cragstan, twirls cane, 1930's.

Left: Celluloid rabbit, 1930–1940. Right: Egg, plastic and tin, 1950's.

Eggs

German, turn of the century.

German, 7", early 1900's.

German Democratic Republic, 1991.

Early 1900's.

Early 1900's.

Early 1900's.

Early 1900's.

Disney character eggs, 1930's.

Late 1800's.

Reverse view of above photo.

Milk glass, blown egg, turn of the century.

Milk glass egg and storage basket, 1880–1890.

Goebel, German.

2¼", 1960's.

Musical, Mattel, Inc., 1950's.

Small, 1920's. Large, 1940's.

Turn of century and early 1900's.

Egg carton and Styrofoam eggs, 1970's.

Left: Plastic eggs, 1960's. Right: Flocked plastic eggs, 1980's.

Handpainted, 1950's.

Pip squeaks, Grand Toys, 1960's.

Chicks and Ducklings

Left: Avon, 1990. Right: Plastic chick and cart, 1940's.

Chalk chicks, 1930's. Tin, by Lowette, 1920–1930's.

Left: Chalk chicks with waxed cup candy container, 1940's. Right: Easter chick boxes, 1940's.

Papier-maché hen on nest, Burt Co., 1920's.

Left: Ceramic chick, 1970's. Middle: Gibson Greetings, Inc., 1980's. Right: Flocked chick, 1940's.

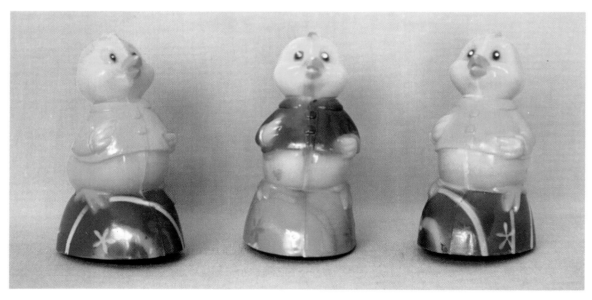

Plastic chick roll toys, by Easter Unlimited, 1960's.

Cotton chicks, 1940's.

Cotton chicks and basket. Candy container, cotton covered duck with felt apron.
Whistle, cotton chicks on log. All 1920–1930's.

BASKETS

Plastic basket candy container, 1940–1950's.

Easter baskets, 1940–1950's.

Plastic basket, food stuff container, 1980's.

Metal baskets, made in U.S. of America, 1940's.

Hand crocheted basket, 1990's.

Wicker baskets, 1940's. Rabbit, made in China, 1991.

Easter baskets, 1920–1930's.

Paper Items

Easter greeting card, 1930's.

Uncle Wiggily books, 1940's.

Left: Candy box, 1950's.
Right: Candy container, paper features, Flavour Candy Candy Co., 1950's.

"The Tale of Peter Rabbit," written by Edna M. Aldredge and Jessie F. McKee.
Published by the Harter Publishing Co., 1931.

Made entirely from old comic books, unique.

Magazine, dated April, 1900.

"Ideals" by Ideal Publishing Co.

Easter greeting postcards, all right after the turn of the century.

Candy Box, mint condition, 1940's.

Fold-up Easter decoration, 1940's.

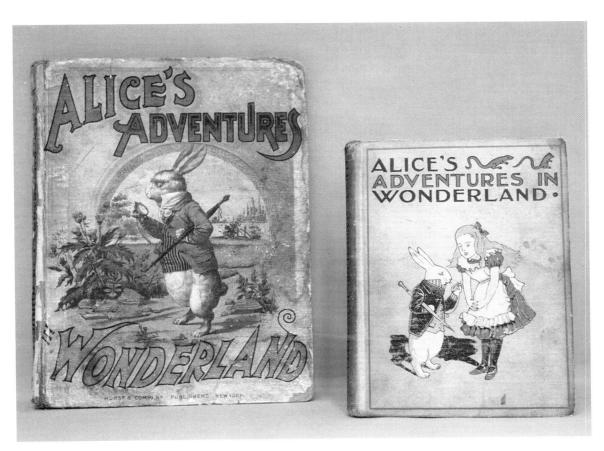

Books, early 1900's.

Children's books, "Playtime Stories," early 1900.

Miscellaneous Items

Top: child's cutters, 1930's. Red plastic bunny cutter, 1970–1980's.
Bottom: metal rabbit cutters, 1930's. Box Aunt Chicks Happy Day's cookie cutters, 1950's.

Peter Rabbit lunch pail, 1920's.

Kauffman's egg dye box, early 1900's. Egg dye packs, 1930–1940's.

Wood puzzles, 4½", made in England, 1940's.

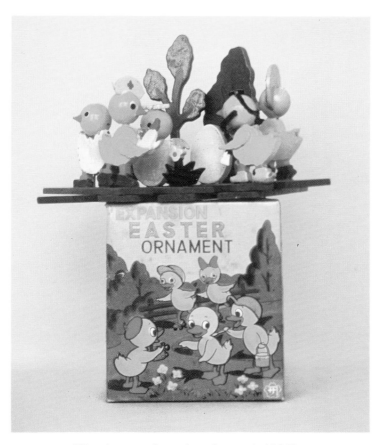

Wood expand toy, handcarved, 1930's.

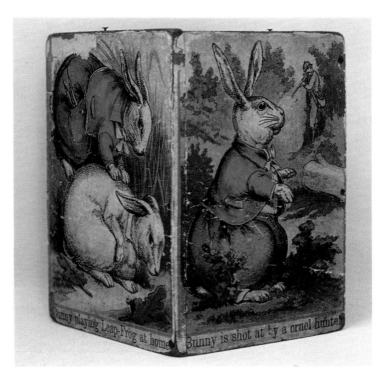

Wood block, one of a set, early 1900's.

Chocolate molds, early 1900's.

Tins, all recent.

Advertising giveaway, C.D. Kenny, early 1900's.

Tin, made in China, 1980's.

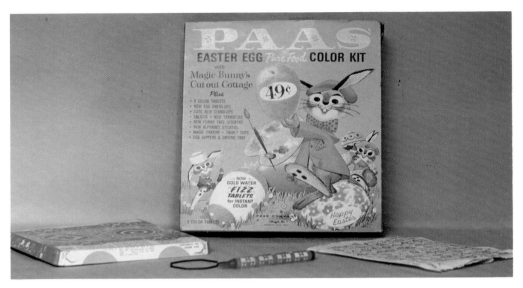

Easter egg color kit with dippers, magic crayon and transfers, 1960's.

Puzzle, "Bonnie and Bunnie," 1940's.

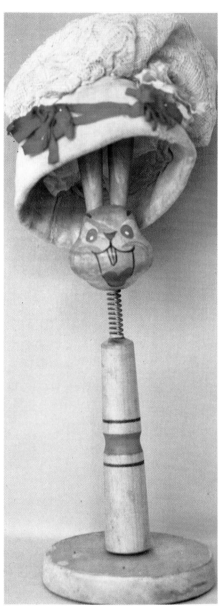

Wood nodder used as
childs hat rack, 1950's.

Candy container, mesh body; 1920's.

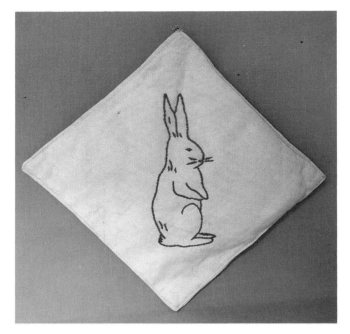

Pot holder, handmade, embroidered rabbit, 1940's.

Egg Factory, made from kit, 1970.

Mug, German, early 1900's.

Left: Reproduction tin, recent. Right: Easter card, 1908.

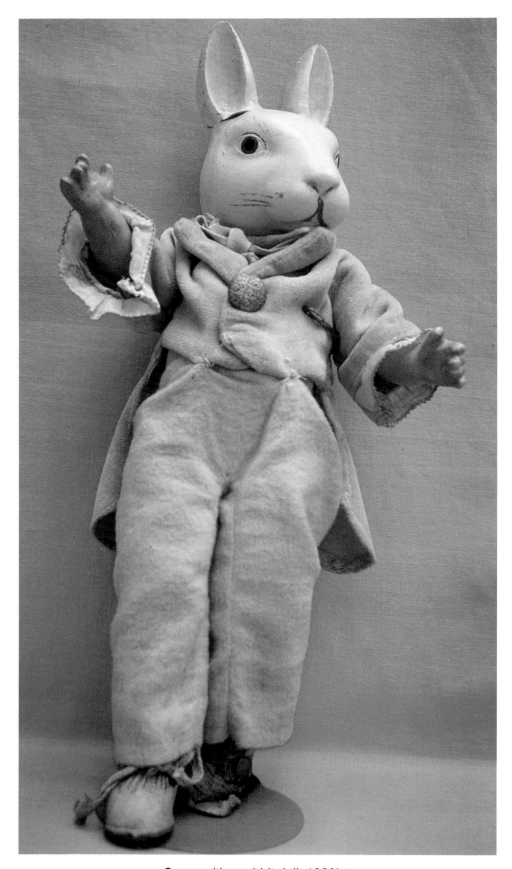

Composition rabbit doll, 1920's.

Bank, Huron Products Co., 1960's.

"HAPPY HUNTING!"

Value Guide

The prices in this guide are an approximate evaluation for articles in good condition. Condition is the primary factor in assessing value.

PAGE 13
Top, Left: 150.00-200.00
Right: 75.00-125.00
Bottom, Left: 300.00-350.00
Right:..50.00

PAGE 14
Top 210.00
Bottom, Left: 150.00
Right: 75.00-95.00

PAGE 15 ....100.00-150.00

PAGE 16 ....200.00-250.00

PAGE 17 ....150.00

PAGE 18 ....35.00-45.00

PAGE 19
Top ....15.00 ea.
Bottom 35.00-45.00

PAGE 20
Top, Left:..15.00
Middle: 5.00
Right:...15.00
Bottom 35.00-45.00

PAGE 21 ....50.00-75.00

PAGE 22 Left: 25.00
Right: 25.00

PAGE 23 ....100.00-125.00

PAGE 24
Top 150.00-200.00
Bottom 100.00

PAGE 25 ....500.00-550.00 pair

PAGE 26 Rabbit:..250.00
Cart: 125.00

PAGE 27 Left:..35.00-40.00
Right: 20.00-25.00

PAGE 28
Top, Left:..15.00
Middle: 5.00
Right:...25.00
Bottom ....35.00-45.00 ea.

PAGE 29
Top 375.00-500.00

PAGE 84
  Top ....20.00 ea.
  Bottom ....8.00-10.00 ea.

PAGE 85
  Top ....25.00-35.00 ea.
  Bottom, Large: ....20.00 ea.
    Small: ....15.00 ea.

PAGE 86
  Top ....25.00-45.00 ea.
  Bottom ....5.00 dozen

PAGE 87
  Top, Left:...5.00 dozen
    Right:..5.00 dozen
  Bottom ....7.00-10.00 ea.

PAGE 88 ....7.00-10.00 ea.

PAGE 89 Left: 10.00
    Right:..10.00
PAGE 90
  Top, Chicks..10.00 ea.
    Tin 25.00
  Bottom, Left: 15.00-20.00
    Right: 15.00-25.00

PAGE 91 ....65.00-75.00

PAGE 92
  Top, Left:...5.00
    Middle: 5.00
    Right:..10.00
  Bottom ....10.00 ea.

PAGE 93
  Top ....5.00-10.00 ea.
  Bottom, Chicks and basket 20.00
    Candy container 55.00-65.00
    Whistle 45.00

PAGE 94 ....20.00

PAGE 95 ....10.00-15.00 ea.

PAGE 96 ....5.00

PAGE 97
  Top ....15.00-25.00 ea.
  Bottom 8.00-10.00

PAGE 98 Baskets ....15.00-25.00 ea.
    Rabbit 8.00-10.00

PAGE 99 ....10.00-20.00 ea.

PAGE 100 ....15.00-20.00

PAGE 101
  Top ....10.00-15.00 ea.
  Bottom, Left: 10.00-15.00
    Right: 15.00-25.00

PAGE 102 ....15.00-20.00

126

Schroeder's Antiques Price Guide

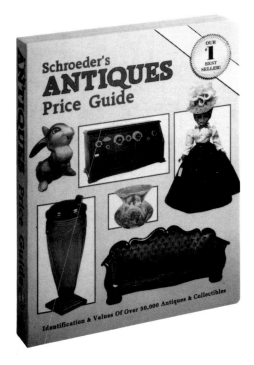

Schroeder's Antiques Price Guide has become THE household name in the antiques & collectibles field. Our team of editors works year-round with more than 200 contributors to bring you our #1 best-selling book on antiques & collectibles.

With more than 50,000 items identified & priced, Schroeder's is a must for the collector & dealer alike. If it merits the interest of today's collector, you'll find it in Schroeder's. Each subject is represented with histories and background information. In addition, hundreds of sharp original photos are used each year to illustrate not only the rare and unusual, but the everyday "fun-type" collectibles as well — not postage stamp pictures, but large close-up shots that show important details clearly.

Our editors compile a new book each year. Never do we merely change prices. Accuracy is our primary aim. Prices are gathered over the entire year previous to publication, from ads and personal contacts. Then each category is thoroughly checked to spot inconsistencies, listings that may not be entirely reflective of actual market dealings, and lines too vague to be of merit. Only the best of the lot remains for publication. You'll find Schroeder's Antiques Price Guide the one to buy for factual information and quality.

No dealer, collector or investor can afford not to own this book. It is available from your favorite bookseller or antiques dealer at the low price of $12.95. If you are unable to find this price guide in your area, it's available from Collector Books, P.O. Box 3009, Paducah, KY 42002-3009 at $12.95 plus $2.00 for postage and handling.

8½ x 11", 608 Pages   **$12.95**

COLLECTOR BOOKS
A Division of Schroeder Publishing Co., Inc.